# Developing Citizenship

## ACTIVITIES FOR PERSONAL, SOCIAL AND HEALTH EDUCATION

# year

## Christine Moorcroft

# A & C BLACK

# Contents

## How do rules and laws affect me?

## Respect for property

## Local democracy for young citizens

## In the media – what's the news?

Published 2005 by A & C Black Publishers Limited
37 Soho Square, London W1D 3QZ
www.acblack.com

ISBN–10: 0-7136-7121-1
ISBN–13: 978-0-7136-7121-6

'All puffed out' adapted from *Daily Mirror*, 16 Nov 2004
© Mirrorpix 2004, reproduced courtesy of Mirrorpix.
Every effort has been made to trace copyright holders and to obtain permission for use of copyright material. The authors and publishers would be pleased to rectify any error or omission in future editions.

The author and publishers would like to thank Catherine Yemm and Roy Honeybone for their assistance in producing this book.

A CIP catalogue record for this book is available from the British Library.

Printed in Great Britain by St Edmundsbury Press, Bury St Edmunds, Suffolk.

A & C Black uses paper produced with elemental chlorine-free pulp, harvested from managed sustainable forests.

# Introduction

**Developing Citizenship** is a series of seven photocopiable activity books for Citizenship lessons (including Personal, Social and Health Education and, in the foundation stage, *Personal, social and emotional development*). Each book provides a range of activities to help teachers to prepare children to play an active role as citizens, including:

- developing confidence and responsibility and making the most of their abilities;
- developing a healthy, safe lifestyle;
- developing good relationships and respecting differences between people;
- thinking for themselves, expressing their own thoughts and opinions confidently, and listening to others' points of view;
- becoming full members of the groups they belong to, knowing they have rights but also becoming increasingly aware of their responsibilities.

The activities in **Year 5** are based on the QCA Scheme of Work for Citizenship at Key Stages 1 and 2 and support children's development in the following areas:

- understanding themselves as individuals and members of their communities;
- learning basic rules and skills for keeping themselves healthy and safe, and for behaving well;
- taking responsibility for themselves and their environment;
- understanding their own and other people's feelings;
- awareness of the views, needs and rights of other people;
- social skills such as taking turns, sharing, playing, helping others, resolving simple arguments and resisting bullying;
- participating in the life of their school and neighbourhood.

The activities are linked with other areas of the curriculum where appropriate. Teachers are encouraged to use them to support the development of children's roles as members of their class, school and neighbourhood communities: for example, the children can help to organise their classroom, organise fund-raising events for a local charity or find out how to influence their local council.

Each activity sheet features a **Teachers' note** at the foot of the page, which may be masked before photocopying. Expanded teaching notes are provided in the **Notes on the activities** on pages 5–12. Most of the activity sheets end with a challenge (**Now try this!**) which reinforces and extends the children's learning and provides the teacher with an opportunity for assessment. These activities might be appropriate for only a few children; it is not expected that the whole class should complete them. A separate sheet of paper will be needed for some extension activities.

## Beyond the classroom

The series takes into account that unplanned experiences which the children have at school and in other places can contribute to the development of concepts and attitudes concerning citizenship. To help teachers to link children's learning through taught activities with their learning at other times, the teachers' notes make suggestions wherever possible for promoting the development of citizenship outside lesson times.

## Organisation

The activities require very few resources beyond pencils, scissors, card and other general classroom items. Any other materials you will need are specified in the **Notes on the activities** (for example, computers, information books and leaflets, pictures, newspapers and fiction books).

## Vocabulary

Key vocabulary to be introduced is provided in the **Notes on the activities**.

## Health and safety

**Developing Citizenship** provides advice on how to make lessons safe and how to encourage children to take responsibility for their own safety. Specific health and safety notes are included in the **Notes on the activities** where appropriate. Advice on implementing safe policy and practice for the use of the Internet in schools can be found on the British Educational Communications and Technology Agency's website: www.becta.org.uk.

## Useful websites

**Citizenship education curriculum**: www.dfes.gov.uk/citizenship (summarises the citizenship curriculum, offers free resources for teachers, links to the QCA schemes of work)

**Institute for Citizenship**: www.citizen.org.uk/education (ideas for classroom activities; links to websites offering useful information)

**Citizenship Foundation**: www.citizenshipfoundation.org.uk (aims to support education about the law, democracy and society)

**Association for Citizenship Teaching**: www.teachingcitizenship.org.uk (a professional association for citizenship teachers)

**Virtual Teacher Centre**: http://curriculum.becta.org.uk/docserver.php?docid=6653 (information and resources for citizenship teachers; links include downloadable lesson plans)

**Community Service Volunteers**: www.csv.org.uk (supports initiatives in volunteering and training)

**Council for Education in World Citizenship**: www.cewc.org (aims to involve students, teachers and other citizens in taking responsibility for the world's future)

**School Councils UK**: www.schoolcouncils.org (advice on how to set up and run school councils)

**Personal Finance Education Group**: www.pfeg.org (aims to develop financial capability in young people)

**4Learning**: www.channel4.com/learning/microsites/C/citizenship (citizenship resources and TV listings)

# Notes on the activities

The notes in this section expand upon those provided at the foot of each activity sheet. They give ideas for making the most of the sheet, including suggestions for a whole-class introduction, a plenary session or for follow-up work.

To help teachers to select appropriate learning experiences for their pupils, the activities are grouped into sections within each book, but the pages need not be presented in the order in which they appear unless stated otherwise. Ideas for differentiation are suggested in the extension activities and in the notes below.

Where appropriate, stories, poems or non-fiction sources such as newspaper reports, Internet articles or advertisements are suggested for introducing the activities or rounding them off.

## Taking part

These activities develop skills of communication, participation in decision-making activities and contribution to school life beyond the curriculum. They build on work from **Year 4**. The Childline website www.childline.co.uk offers useful advice on communication skills and relationships with others.

**To walk or not to walk** (page 13) develops the children's ability to listen to a partner and to share their views on a topical issue. Invite them to report back to the class the two points from their discussion which they think are the most important. Factors they could consider include the distance walked, the time their parents or carers have to be at work, the safety of the route, the weather and what they have to carry to school. This can be linked with work in geography on mapping, measuring distances, using co-ordinates and drawing to scale.

> **Vocabulary:** *discussion, factor, influence, issue.*

In **Action for activity: 1** and **2** (pages 14–15) the children hold a discussion with another person in which they offer their own opinions and take on board the views of the other person concerning an issue connected with healthy lifestyles. They then collaborate in a group to make a decision. An active way of travelling to school could involve using bikes or wheelchairs where appropriate. The children are asked to consider any problems they might face in travelling to school and to come up with solutions to one of them: for example, if the distance is too far to travel alone, they could ask the school to organise 'walking buses' which could be joined at different points along the route for safety, adults could organise a rota to accompany groups of children on foot and to push trolleys to carry heavy school bags. Ask the children how they decided which problem to choose for page 15. Did they agree, compromise or take a vote? Do those groups who tackle the extension activity think everyone would agree with their solution? The question of the value of exercise can be linked with work in science (keeping healthy).

> **Vocabulary:** *brainstorm, decision, problem, solution, transport.*

**Into action** (page 16) develops the children's ability to work effectively as a group and to reach a group decision about a topical issue. The activity could be altered so that it is based on a real road safety issue affecting the children: for example, lack of footpath, poor lighting, speed of vehicles, crossing places, dog-fouling, areas of potential for bullying, and so on. They should consider how their proposed solutions would affect other people, including motorists. The activity can be linked with work in geography and science.

> **Vocabulary:** *agree, disagree, hazard, motorist, opinion, pedestrian, problem, safety, solution, support, survey, through route, vehicle.*

## Choices

This section provides opportunities for the children to develop an awareness of the choices they can make, their rights and responsibilities and how to make the best decisions in different situations. The activities can be linked with work in RE on right and wrong and are appropriate for introduction through circle time.

**These things matter** (page 17) encourages the children to share their opinions on things that are important to them. They could answer the questions individually and then share their answers with a partner or interview a partner to find his or her opinions. The extension activity requires a more detailed interview of a partner.

> **Vocabulary:** *discuss, explanation, important, improve, listen, matter, opinion.*

**Think about it** and **Recycle it** (pages 18–19) encourage the children to consider alternatives when they make decisions and to explain their choices. Consequences to consider include: danger to animals which can become trapped in plastic bags or containers, cut themselves on sharp edges or eat substances which poison them; untidiness and unpleasantness in the environment; and harm to people's health or risk of injury from materials such as broken glass. They could also consider the work created for people and whether or not this is a good thing and the effects of burning fuel to provide transport for disposing of rubbish or recycling it. You could introduce page 19 by showing a collection of objects and materials which are commonly thrown away and sorting them according to whether or not they can be recycled. The websites of local councils can be used to find out about the different materials and objects which can be recycled and re-used. A useful website for finding any local government site is www.oultwood.com. This would enable children to investigate what is happening elsewhere. See also: Organic Recycling www.organicrecycling.ndo.co.uk, Recycle More www.recycle-more.co.uk, Waste Watch www.wastewatch.org.uk, ActionAid's project for recycling mobile phones and printer cartridges www.actionaidrecycling.org.uk/cartridge guide1.htm, Oxfam's mobile phone recycling project www.oxfam.org.uk/what_you_can_do/recycle/phones.htm and the Vision Aid project for recycling pairs of glasses www.charityfreebies.co.uk/old-glasses.htm. Higher-attaining children working on page 18 could use graphics software to design a poster in which pictures and text can be altered according to the audience for which it is intended. Some children could compile a directory of recycling in which they list recyclable goods and materials in alphabetical order and give contact details for local places where they can be recycled. This could be stored as a table in a word-processing program to be added to as the children come across new facilities.

> **Vocabulary:** *consequences, environment, recycle, re-use.*

**Chocolate choice** (page 20) is about how the choices we make can affect other people. It encourages the children to consider where their money goes when they buy a bar of chocolate and whether the cocoa growers get a fair price. The FAIRTRADE Mark is a certification label awarded to products from developing countries which meet recognised standards of fair trade. It ensures fair prices for produce, facilitates the development of farming communities and gives workers a say in social development on plantations. Fairtrade was launched in the Netherlands in response to the collapse of world coffee prices in 1988. Since then Fairtrade labels have been launched in many other countries and for different products, including cocoa and tea. Teachers can find out from the Fairtrade Foundation (www.fairtrade.org.uk) about the experiences of some of the growers and producers. The children could find out more from Christian Aid's 'Global Gang' website www.globalgang.org.uk/homeworkhelp/chocolate. The Christian Aid main site runs a campaign to promote fair trade: www.christian-aid.org.uk/learn/schools/chocolate/index. The following US site is also useful: www.globalexchange.org/campaigns/fairtrade/cocoa/chocolatekids.html. You could ask higher-attaining children why child labour cannot simply be banned. Give them five minutes to think about it before they answer. This activity can be linked with work in geography (Connecting ourselves to the world).

> **Vocabulary:** *affect, choice, decision, effect, fair, grower, plantation, producer, trade, unfair.*

**Making a difference** (page 21) encourages the children to investigate and consider alternatives when making decisions and to explain their choices. It also provides an opportunity for them to make choices which help people in the developing world to make a living. Ask them if they had heard of Fairtrade before they began this or page 20. This page could be used to conduct a survey of local retailers and shoppers to find out how much Fairtrade produce is available locally and how many people know about it and buy it. This could lead to the selling of Fairtrade goods in the school snack shop. It could be linked to work in maths on money and percentages.

> **Vocabulary:** *affect, choice, decision, effect, fair, goods, grower, producer, retailer, shopper, stock, trade, unfair.*

**Time to sell** (page 22) is about evaluating the ways in which the media present information to their target audience. It focuses on television advertisements and requires a video recording of television advertisements from specific times of the day: for example, early morning, mid-morning, mid-afternoon, early evening. Ask the children if they notice any similarities or differences between the goods advertised at different times. Are any goods advertised at several different times? Are some goods advertised only at certain times? Discuss why this is, focusing on who is likely to be watching television (and who is not) at those times. Discuss which groups of people are likely to

buy (or ask others to buy) certain items. When are the most toys advertised? When are the most items for elderly people advertised? Why? Some children could make graphs on which to present their findings: for example, to show the number of different types of advertisements shown on a Saturday morning. Teachers could find out more from the Advertising Standards Authority website: www.asab.org.uk/asa. Link this with literacy (reading and writing promotional texts).

> **Vocabulary:** *advertise, advertisement, attract, attractive, audience, goods, promotional, purchaser, target, user.*

# Animals and us

The activities in this section develop the idea of rights and responsibilities. They draw on the children's learning from **Year 4** on the needs of animals. The activities explore animal welfare and the responsibilities of humans towards animals and could be developed through contact with local branches of animal welfare organisations.

**Zoo talk** (page 23) is about the responsibilities humans have towards animals. This could be introduced by a visit to a zoo or developed from the children's experiences of zoos. During the plenary session invite feedback from each group before the children vote on the issue of whether or not it is wrong to keep animals in zoos. Issues to discuss include: protecting species threatened with extinction, educating the public, scientific research, animal welfare, public safety and animals bred in captivity. Link this with work in literacy on writing arguments and with geography (Passport to the world) and science (Life cycles).

> **Vocabulary:** *argument, ballot, debate, discussion, summary, vote.*

**Hedgehog helper** and **Hedgehog-friendly school** (pages 24–25) encourage the children to contribute ideas to a discussion and to listen to those of others. They are also about animal welfare and people's responsibilities for animals in the wild. The passage could be read as a shared text by children who need help in reading it. Others could read it individually or with a partner. Ask them what facts they have found out about hedgehogs. What are the main dangers to hedgehogs? The children could work individually or in groups to write a list of suggestions about how people can care for hedgehogs. Page 25 could be linked with an investigation of the school grounds to find out how hedgehog-friendly they are. It provides an opportunity to encourage the children to take an active part in discussion with adults involved with the school and with decision-making at school. They could present their findings about hedgehogs to people who look after the school grounds, showing how hedgehogs can be beneficial to gardens (they eat slugs and many other invertebrates which feed on plants) and how they can be encouraged and protected. Ask them to consider how they will present their ideas to other people and how to encourage other people to look after hedgehogs. Wild animal welfare websites include:
   Prickly Ball Farm & Hedgehog Hospital www.hedgehog.org.uk
   Tiggywinkles Wildlife Hospital www.sttiggywinkles.org.uk
   UK Animal Rescuers www.animalrescuers.co.uk/html/ukwild.html
   Animals in Distress Sanctuary www.animals-in-distress.net/wildlife-united-kingdom.htm

This work could draw on **Year 4** science (habitats) and be linked with current work on life cycles. There are also opportunities for links with literacy (writing information texts, explanations and advice).

> **Vocabulary:** *animal welfare, campaign, discussion, hibernate, needs, predator, protection, responsibilities, wildlife.*

**Five freedoms** (page 26) is about the ways in which animal charities can promote animal welfare. Begin by reviewing the children's previous learning about the needs of animals. It will also be useful to discuss the meanings of the words used in the 'Five freedoms', or some children could look these up for themselves. A local vet could provide information about keeping and caring for pets (and perhaps make a visit). It is important for the children to discuss their thoughts before considering the RSPCA's five freedoms. They should be aware that it is acceptable to have different views from those of the RSPCA. Encourage them to communicate with the RSPCA if they feel they have an important point to make: www.rspca.org.uk.

> **Vocabulary:** *discomfort, distress, freedom, hunger, injury, Member of Parliament, thirst.*

# People who help us – the local police

This section is about the work of the police and other local organisations. The activities develop the children's awareness of the work of the police in keeping the community safe and provide opportunities to explore issues of right and wrong, crimes, penalties and punishments. A range of material on citizenship is available from West Yorkshire Police: Community Trust, PO Box 9, Wakefield, WF1 3QP or visit www.westyorkshire.police.uk/section-item.asp?sid=4&iid=293.

**The law in action** (page 27) links work on **Animals and us** with **People who help us – the local police**. It helps the children to learn about issues dealt with by the local police and about how the RSPCA prosecutes people who are cruel to animals. To prepare for this activity the children could collect news articles about cruelty to animals. The RSPCA website (www.rspca.org.uk) has reports of such incidents and how they were resolved. The Newspaper Society provides a useful gateway site to help you to find your regional newspaper's website: www.newspapersoc.org.uk/default.asp?cid=251. The children could compare the outcomes of different cases and discuss whether the punishments were appropriate and fair, what punishments they would have given the offenders, and why. They could also discuss and write about whether the offender's age and experience of animals should be taken into account, and the ways in which the punishment could help them to care for animals better in the future.

> **Vocabulary:** *court, cruel, cruelty, fine, imprisonment, offender, police, prosecute, punishment, RSPCA.*

**Emergency call** (page 28) develops the children's understanding of the work of the police and reinforces their previous learning about when it is appropriate to make emergency calls. It would be useful to review how to make these calls, including the information that would be needed. Also emphasise the problems caused by hoax or unnecessary emergency calls. The information presented on this page is adapted from the advice given to the public in the charter of Britain's Northumbria police force. A visit from the local police's schools liaison officer would be valuable – www.police.uk provides links to all official police forces. This activity could be related to work in literacy: the children could write a story in which a 999 call is made. Their story could be written to point out to younger children when they should not make 999 calls or to explain to others of their own age when it is acceptable to do so. The children should consider what type of language is suitable for their target audience.

> **Vocabulary:** *ambulance, charter, coastguard, collision, congestion, crime, danger, disorder, disturbance, emergency, evidence, fire brigade, in progress, police, vulnerable.*

**Police help** (page 29) is about the work of the police. It focuses on the occasions which are not emergencies when people need the help of the police and how to contact them: for example, if a crime (such as a robbery) has been committed but no one is in danger, valuable property has been lost, information is needed about the law or to report suspicious actions which might be linked to a crime. The children could find out from their local police force's website what the police would do. This can be found through links from www.police.uk. The extension activity can be linked with literacy. The rest of the class could undertake this activity with appropriate support.

> **Vocabulary:** *contact, emergency, non-emergency, police force.*

**Keep out crime** (page 30) is about local schemes for combating crime. It focuses on people's responsibility to protect themselves against crime appropriately. It is useful first to discuss what is meant by some of the precautions suggested on this page: for example, timers, sensors, British Standard door locks, serial numbers, property markers and bank and credit card statements (and why they should not be put into household waste). You could bring in a property marker and show the children how to label valuables. Feedback could be recorded on a large copy of this chart and displayed; the children could later add other ideas about how they could help. Important ways in which they can help include always telling their parents or carers where they are going and with whom (and keeping within the boundaries set by their parents or carers and keeping to agreed times); noticing anything unusual about a neighbour's home (for example, curtains drawn or left open for a few days, no response when delivery drivers call); not seeing a neighbour for several days; keeping an eye on neighbours' homes while they are away; making notes on the appearance of anyone acting suspiciously; writing down the registration numbers, makes and models of parked vehicles; locking and securing their bikes when they park them; closing and locking doors and windows when they go out and keeping them locked while they are indoors; taking their belongings out of the family car or putting them in the boot when it is parked; writing down the serial numbers of, and marking, their own valuables (such as CD players, mobile phones and computers) and keeping the list in a safe place; noticing if adults put bank or credit card statements in the bin and reminding them what could happen (someone could steal them and use the owner's credit card or identity). The children could find out from the local police station about Neighbourhood Watch schemes in their area. Discuss what 'Try to help people when they need it' means and point out that although the children should not as a rule talk to strangers, they should not be discouraged from speaking to an elderly or disabled person who has fallen or dropped something and needs help. This activity could be linked with work in literacy (using descriptive language, writing descriptions, writing recounts and reading and writing suspense or adventure stories). There are also opportunities for links with science and design and technology (using sensors and timers and making models using circuits with sensors and timers).

> **Vocabulary:** *British Standard, crime, neighbourhood, police, prevention, property marker, sensor, serial number, timer.*

**Crime report** (page 31) is about how the children can contribute to, and participate in, community issues. It provides an opportunity to discuss the concerns some people have about reporting crimes or suspected crimes or responding to police appeals for evidence. The children could find out about Crimestoppers, which was set up so that witnesses of crimes or people who can provide evidence to help the police can supply information anonymously (www.crimestoppers-uk.org). During the plenary session it is important to point out that children should not intervene in a situation such as the one depicted (for example, by questioning the people who call at the house) but it could be very helpful to the police (and to the victims of the crime) if they write down as much information and description as possible. Draw out that Yusuf would not have been aware that a crime was being committed and so had no reason to make a 999 call (unless he actually saw someone breaking into the house or had reason to believe that Mrs Nash was being harmed – for example, if he heard screams or shouts or there was any evidence of a scuffle). However, if he thought there was anything suspicious about the visitors he could have told his parents or carers or contacted the police as a non-emergency call. Point out that if the visitors were genuine, they and Mrs Nash would have no reason to object to this – in fact, many people would welcome the care for an elderly friend or relative. Once the crime was discovered, it was essential that he gave as much information as possible to the police (including the time of the visit, descriptions of the people and their vehicle and the registration number). The children could find out more about how the police collect evidence from children, how identity parades are conducted and how the police would act if suspicious activities were reported or if they were investigating a crime in which people entered a place illegally. Ask the children how observant they think they are and set them a test: for example, to describe the makes and models of cars belonging to the teachers which are parked near the school. Are there any cars which are not usually there? As a homework activity for a light evening, ask them to log the movement of unknown cars where they live: make, model, registration number, what the driver and passengers look like, what they are wearing, and so on. Remind them that not every stranger is a criminal and that very few people are actually the victims of crime.

> **Vocabulary:** *burglary, crime, illegal, investigate, suspicious.*

# Living in a diverse world

In this section the children learn about identities and communities. The activities develop their understanding of basic human needs and rights and equality among people, their respect for themselves and others, membership of communities (including school and family) and about the differences and similarities between people. They learn about the importance of respecting one another and that it is wrong to abuse people for any reason, including their race. They explore the characteristics of places and communities and share their findings and ideas with others. The issue of racism can be explored further in circle time.

**Town and country** (page 32) is about different communities and their similarities and differences. Give the children time to discuss their ideas with a partner and then to make notes about the main points of their discussion. Invite feedback. This is an opportunity to explore any stereotyped ideas children have about communities about which they know little. Town schools could set up e-mail links with country schools and vice versa to find out more about their different communities. When the answers to their questions have arrived, encourage the children to discuss the aspects about which they were wrong and why they made these assumptions. Also encourage them to draw out the advantages and disadvantages of living in either type of location. This can be linked with work in geography on mapping and comparing localities.

> **Vocabulary:** *city, cityscape, country, landscape, locality, rural, scenery, surroundings, town, urban, village.*

**A visit to Chinatown** (page 33) helps the children to recognise diversity within their communities. Begin with the children's present knowledge and understanding of Chinese communities in this country. There are opportunities to develop their appreciation of the legacy of Chinese communities (this could be developed further using page 34) and to research where their nearest 'Chinatown' is. They might be familiar with Chinese food, symbols such as the dragon and festivals such as the Chinese New Year. Schools in British cities which have a 'Chinatown' (such as Birmingham, Liverpool, London, Manchester and Newcastle) could enrich this work by arranging a visit to the area to find out about food, shops, culture, festivals, and so on. The children could also find out about Chinese communities (including maps and photographs of the areas, some Chinese words and how they are written in Chinese, culture, lifestyle, food and festivals) from www.chinatown-online.co.uk/pages/guide/index.html. This website has pages which are specially written for children. Ask the children if they would like to visit Chinatown, and why. If possible, arrange a visit to a local Chinese takeaway and ask the children which meals they have tried and which are their favourites. They could find out about the ingredients. Perhaps you could arrange a Chinese meal for the children at school. This activity has links with geography (Connecting ourselves to the world and Geography and numbers) if the children have opportunities to use and draw maps, plan routes and find out what places are like. There are also opportunities to link this with work in art and design (Objects and meanings, Containers and Talking textiles).

> **Vocabulary:** *China, Chinatown, Chinese, community, culture, design, diversity, environment, interdependent, language, race, religion, settlement.*

**Finding out** (page 34) is about the similarities and differences between communities. It could be connected to a visit to Chinatown or to another area with a large community which came to this country from overseas. Encourage the children to find out what makes the community distinctive and special: for example, religion, places of worship, food, the arts, shops, clothing, decoration, entertainment festivals, restaurants or other businesses. Also encourage them to discuss and write questions which will help them to find out more and to consider how they can find the answers. This could lead to a 'Chinese day', 'Indian day', 'African-Caribbean day' or a similar event in which the children display their artwork and prepare special foods and events, possibly with the help of members of the local community. If the local community is predominantly or entirely white (for example, in many rural areas), it is useful to make contact with schools in places with a more diverse community.

> **Vocabulary:** *community, culture, design, diversity, environment, interdependent, language, race, religion.*

**Kick out racism** (page 35) helps the children to develop strategies to deal with prejudice, including racism, and to support others who encounter it. Useful websites about racism issues include: Britkid www.britkid.org, Let's Kick Racism out of Football www.kickitout.org and Show Racism the Red Card www.srtrc.org. Invite volunteers to read the passages aloud. After each passage has been read, ask the class what they think of the incident described. Who was doing wrong and why was it wrong? You could also provide news reports of other racist incidents from sporting events. Examples of what people could have said or done could include: refuse to join in; applaud abused players; write letters expressing disgust to the club fanzine or club chairman; boycott matches involving teams with racist fans and encourage friends to do the same; write letters of complaint to the Football Association (FA), the European Football Union (UEFA) or the International Football Federation (FIFA), according to the level of the match; and write to local or national newspapers condemning racism in sport. Draw out that any racist behaviour must be reported in order to put a stop to it.

> **Vocabulary:** *abuse, disrespect, insult, prejudice, racism, racist, respect.*

# Developing our school grounds

This section involves the children in observation, discussion, problem-solving and co-operation. It develops the children's ability to work in a democratic way which takes into consideration the needs and wishes of the whole community. It can be linked with work in geography (use of maps and plans) and with mathematics (costing projects).

**Accident aware: 1** and **2** (pages 36–37) help the children to develop their roles as members of the school community and to develop skills in consulting with other members of the community and working in groups. The children are likely to be aware of places around the school from which they are barred for safety reasons. The first activity focuses on identifying places and substances and equipment which could be dangerous. It is unlikely that any dangerous objects will be where the children can touch them, but this is an opportunity to show the children why and explain how these are kept secure. Some of them could read the school's health and safety policy and guidelines. They could help to protect younger children by reporting to a teacher any unlocked doors which should be locked or hazardous substances (such as certain cleaning materials) which are left in accessible places. They could also look at the standard warnings used for marking hazardous substances and find out what they mean and how these substances could harm them. (See www.brunelmicroscopes.co.uk/symbols.html and www.le.ac.uk/biology/info/safety/labelling.htm.)

> **Vocabulary:** *accident, discussion, hazard, hazardous, health, minimise, precaution, responsibility, risk, safety, substance, survey, temporary.*

**Over to you** (page 38) encourages the children to think about the school environment and to generate and explore ideas about how they can use it safely and how it can be improved with regard to safety: for example, through the use of signs and rules. Draw out that the safety of an environment depends on the co-operation of the people who use it as well as on the people who manage it.

> **Vocabulary:** *accident, behaviour, co-operation, discussion, environment, planning, safety.*

**Cost it** (page 39) helps the children to learn about the costs and limitations of their plans. It could be introduced using an example: the children of one school had to walk along a road with no pavements which was also used by vehicles. There was a school crossing patrol on the main road from which this minor road led, but children crossed the minor road in various places. Their ideas included building a pavement at one side of the road and putting in a zebra crossing, but when they costed these they were found to be very expensive. One group then suggested painting a track at one side of the road along which the children should walk, including one place only where they should cross the road; to make it look interesting and to make its purpose clear, especially to younger children, they suggested that the track should be marked in brightly-coloured footprints. The headteacher and school governor agreed that it was feasible and encouraged the children to write to the local council to ask permission to have the footprints painted along the road. The council agreed and arranged to have the work done. The children then wrote and thanked them and sent feedback about how well the new system was working. There are links with literacy here (writing letters in the appropriate style of language and level of formality). The children also develop their mathematical skills when they compare the costs of their plans. Discuss whether the cheapest solution is necessarily the best.

> **Vocabulary:** *communication, consult, consultation, cost, environment, negotiation, permission, plan, safety.*

# Children's rights – human rights

This section is about human rights and needs. It develops the children's understanding of fairness and justice and about the meaning of prejudice. The children learn about the United Nations Convention on the Rights of the Child, that it applies to all children, and how. They learn to recognise whether children's rights are being upheld.

**Charter of rights** (page 40) is about basic human rights and how they apply to children in particular. It encourages the children to review what they know about their rights and to express them in the form of a charter. They could first look up and discuss the meaning of *charter*. Draw out that a charter is an agreement made by a group of people or organisations such as countries in which they promise to abide by a set of conditions or rules. Invite feedback from the children and encourage them to think of the rights and needs children have which differ from those of adults. In the plenary session, collate all the groups' suggestions and discuss which of the rights listed the children think are the most important. In another lesson, the groups who tackled the extension activity could make their presentations to the class.

> **Vocabulary:** *charter, conditions, promise, rights, uphold.*

**The rights of the child** (page 41) is about human rights and what is fair and unfair. The children have the opportunity to read an adapted version, in simple language, of the United Nations Convention on the Rights of the Child and to compare it with their own list of rights. Invite feedback when they have had a chance to write about how these rights help things to be fair. Do they think all children's rights are upheld? They might be able to think of situations they have seen on the television news or read in newspapers where children's rights were not upheld. The children might not know about the minimum ages at which they can work, for how long and when. (Children are not permitted to work before the age of 13 and there are rules about how long they are allowed to work and when.) You could help the children to find out more from www.right-to-education.org/content/age/uk.html. UNICEF has a special young person's website www.therightssite.org.uk where the children can learn about children's rights worldwide (including case studies and suggestions for action). Free comics are available for schools from the UNICEF helpdesk (0870 606 3377). The Children's Rights Alliance for England champions the rights of the child and lobbies the UK government on children's issues (see www.crae.org.uk).

> **Vocabulary:** *charter, convention, cruelty, dignity, disability, exploitation, minimum age, protection, responsibility, rights, tolerance, United Nations.*

**ActionAid** and **Children's responsibilities** (pages 42–43) help the children to apply what they have learned about human rights – particularly the rights of children – to different situations and to understand that rights come with responsibilities. They find out how charitable organisations such as ActionAid help to uphold children's rights in developing countries. This could be linked with work in geography (Connecting ourselves to the world). On page 43 they identify some of the responsibilities children have and how they are linked to their rights.

> **Vocabulary:** *charity, responsibility, rights, uphold.*

**That's a lie** (page 44) develops the children's understanding of right and wrong. It focuses on situations in which children sometimes tell lies, and why they do so. You could introduce the topic by reading Hilaire Belloc's poem *Matilda (Who Told Lies and Was Burned to Death)*, which can be found in *Selected Cautionary Verses* (Puffin Books). Draw out that the children's lies in the example on the sheet could put them at risk because their parents do not know where they are. They are wrong to go somewhere without their parents' knowledge and they are wrong to lie about it. They are also abusing their parents' trust and going to a place where they are not allowed alone for safety reasons. By abusing this trust they are being dishonest and they are also jeopardising what they will be allowed to do at other times.

> **Vocabulary:** *dangerous, dishonest, honest, lie, safe, trust, truth, unsafe.*

**The bully: 1** and **2** (pages 45–46) focus on bullying and the nature of aggression. Ask the children how they feel towards Bill Craddock. Would they feel sorry for him if he had bullied them? Draw out the reasons why some people bully others and whether being friendly towards them while they are not bullying might help. The children could find out more about the reasons for bullying and what to do if they are bullied (or someone else they know is bullied) from the following websites:

Kidscape www.kidscape.org.uk
Bullying Online www.bullying.co.uk
Childline www.childline.org.uk/extra/bullyingindex.asp
BBC Schools www.bbc.co.uk/schools/bullying
Antibully www.antibully.org.uk

Useful books include *Bullies Are a Pain in the Brain* by Trevor Romain (Free Spirit Publishing) and *The Willow Street Kids Beat the Bullies* by Michele Elliott (Kidscape). As an extension activity the children could be given a plan of their school and then a map of the local area and asked to highlight places where they do not feel safe. Ask them why not. What could be done to make these places safe? To whom can they turn for help? The children could also find other poems which cover the topic of bullying.

> **Vocabulary:** *aggression, bully, fair, understanding, unfair.*

# How do rules and laws affect me?

This section introduces the need for rules and laws in a community in order to protect people's rights and develops the children's understanding of democracy, including how people can be involved in decision-making. They discuss rules and laws and learn how to make suggestions and changes. This could be connected with the school or class council.

**Ground rules** (page 47) is about rules and why we need them. It provides an opportunity to review the children's previous learning about the ground rules for discussions. Examples of ground rules for discussions include: *Listen when someone is speaking, Look at the person who is speaking, Encourage others to have their say, Do not make anyone feel pressurised into speaking, Give others a chance to speak, Think before you speak, Respect others' opinions*. For the extension activity, group processes can be explored and discussed: for example, groups might elect their own chair, scribe and spokesperson to ensure everyone shares equally in a discussion.

> **Vocabulary:** *discussion, ground rules, listen, respect.*

**Democracy** and **Democracy in action** (pages 48–49) develop the children's understanding of the meaning of democracy and how people can take part in decision-making, especially in the making of rules and laws. Ask the children if they think everyone should be asked what they think each time a decision has to be made. Draw out that this is not practical but that in a democratic society people can elect others to act on their behalf; however, they may still be consulted over certain important decisions. The children could write their own 'manifesto' and discuss it with a partner. You could use page 49 after an incident which school rules did not address adequately or when rules have been disobeyed.

> **Vocabulary:** *ballot, community, decision-making, democracy, democratic, elect, election, nominee, representative, rule, school council, vote.*

**Criminal record** (page 50) is about how a criminal record can affect an individual's career. The children might not have realised that, in England and Wales, when they reach the age of ten (eight in Scotland) they have reached the age of criminal responsibility. Until the age of ten the law says that a child cannot be held responsible for a crime. Between the ages of ten and fourteen children can be convicted of a criminal offence if the prosecution can show they were aware that what they were doing was seriously wrong; and they can be given prison sentences. After the age of fourteen the law considers them to be fully responsible for their actions in the same way as an adult, and they are treated as adults in a court of law in terms of criminal responsibility (although not in terms of sentencing). In this activity Lisa might find it difficult to find work anywhere where there are opportunities to steal, but she might be given a chance if she applies for other kinds of work. Zul might be trusted to work in a shop under supervision. Gwyneth's criminal record might have been 'spent' by the time she applies for a university place, in which case she will not have to mention it on her application. The children can find out more about criminal responsibility, sentencing and when sentences become 'spent' from the following websites:

Rizer www.rizer.co.uk/access/default.asp?pg=info
Apex Trust www.apextrust.com
Criminal Records Bureau www.crb.gov.uk

> **Vocabulary:** *criminal, criminal record, prison sentence, responsibility.*

**Shoplifted** (page 51) focuses on one of the ways in which young people tend to break the law – shoplifting – and how it affects both shopkeepers and the local community. It could be introduced by showing the children signs which ban groups of more than three schoolchildren from entering a shop and ban unaccompanied children. Ask them why shopkeepers put up signs like these. Draw out that it is usually because they have had goods stolen by children and are better able to see what is going on if fewer children come into the shop at any one time. How do the children feel when they go into shops displaying signs like this? Draw out that because some children shoplift, all children are regarded by shopkeepers as potential shoplifters. The children could read the story of Mr Shah from *You, Me, Us!* (a Citizenship Foundation resource); see www.citizenshipfoundation.org.uk/main/resource.php?s116.

> **Vocabulary:** *affect, community, consequences, effects, law, offender, shoplift, steal, theft, victim.*

# Respect for property

These activities encourage the children to think about respect for shared property, including school property and property belonging to the local community as well as the property of individuals. They learn to consider the consequences of vandalism and theft.

**Red-handed** (page 52) provides a link between work on **How do rules and laws affect me?** and **Respect for property**. It is about the consequences of shoplifting and encourages the children to use their imagination to understand the experiences of others. The activity invites them to try to see things first from Mrs O'Marr's point of view and then to imagine how Nina might be affected by Mrs O'Marr's decision. Mrs O'Marr could give Nina the opportunity to change her mind about stealing the sweets by asking her if there is anything she has forgotten to pay for. This might make Nina think twice about shoplifting again. She could accuse Nina of shoplifting, phone the police or contact Nina's parents or carers. Nina might be forced to stop shoplifting if her parents stop her going to shops or if she is arrested, or she might realise that she has done wrong and decide of her own accord

not to do it again. If Mrs O'Marr does not report her, she might feel guilty and be sorry for what she has done. What if she did it again? Should Mrs O'Marr give her another chance? It is useful to point out that many shopkeepers may be so fed up with shoplifters that they are not willing to give them a second chance under any circumstances and will ring the police straight away.

> **Vocabulary:** *affect, community, consequences, effects, shoplift, sorry, steal, theft, wrong.*

**Open space** (page 53) encourages the children to respect property in the community. Through photographing or sketching a small open space near the school and discussing its features they can learn to appreciate what this place means to people and how they use it.

> **Vocabulary:** *community, facilities, property, responsibility, shared.*

**Damage survey** and **Vandal busters** (pages 54–55) are about the consequences of crimes and encourage the children to reflect on the effects of vandalism. This could be related to a study of the way in which a local place is used (see page 53). What kinds of vandalism affect this place or could affect it? How would these spoil it for the people who use it? Page 55 invites the children to work as a group to come up with ideas for preventing vandalism. These could include surveillance using cameras or people, securing the place after dark (using fences and locked gates), installing tough 'vandal-proof' benches and other equipment, using tough punishments for vandals or requiring them to contribute towards the cost of repairing the damage and helping with the work.

> **Vocabulary:** *community, damage, facilities, property, responsibility, shared, vandalism.*

# Local democracy for young citizens

Through these activities the children learn to appreciate their local community, the work of the local council and how it serves the community. They find out how local democracy works and how they can contribute.

**Changing places** and **Facilities survey** (pages 56–57) provide opportunities to discuss the local area with a range of people in school and in the local community and to discover their views about it and what it could be like in the future. They consider the existing facilities and others from which the area would benefit. They could record, sort and present their findings using data-handling software.

*Health and safety: The children should question people only under adult supervision. Warn them not to go to anywhere alone and approach strangers to ask them questions.*

> **Vocabulary:** *facility, local community, survey.*

**Local council** (page 58) encourages the children to find out about what a local council is for and how it serves the community. There are two main types of local council – those in built-up city areas and those outside these areas. Authorities in the built-up areas of cities are usually known as *metropolitan borough councils* or *metropolitan district councils*. Those outside the cities in England and Wales are known as *county councils*. Sometimes there are also *parish councils*, which are based in small towns and villages and are sometimes known as *town councils*. The responsibilities of local councils usually include refuse collection, housing, traffic, roads, local planning, social services, education, libraries, leisure and amenities, tourism, entertainment, environmental health, police and fire services as well as electoral registration and consumer protection. They are responsible for granting planning permission for shops and other businesses and any new building. Water supply is the responsibility of the local water company, monitored by the Environment Agency. The children can find out more from the local council's website and from http://youthinformation.com. Most councils produce a leaflet with information about their annual expenditure, usually enclosed with the annual council tax bill. This would be a good source of information for this activity. The children could find out about services provided elsewhere from www.oultwood.com. Are there services which the local council must provide? Which services are optional? Who provides the service if the council does not? How is it funded?

> **Vocabulary:** *amenity, council, councillor, facility, local.*

**Councillor** (page 59) helps the children to learn about what councillors do. A councillor represents a particular ward or small area which he or she knows well. Councillors are elected during local elections in which anyone aged 18 and over who is on the local electoral roll can vote: they serve for four years. They are expected to attend council committee meetings and to vote on important issues. Many local councillors hold a 'surgery' on a regular basis and can be contacted by e-mail. The children could present questions to their councillors in this way should a visit not be possible. The surgeries are often at weekends and adult support/co-operation would be needed. They may like to challenge councillors on the significance of the 'party'. On what issues do councillors have a 'free' vote or must they always follow their party line? The children could also find out how long it takes to put ideas into practice: for example, when a member of the public comes up with a suggestion or complaint.

> **Vocabulary:** *committee, council, councillor, elect, election, electoral roll, local, vote, ward.*

**Debate it** (page 60) involves the children in researching, discussing and debating a topical issue. This activity is based on a real issue on which residents of Hexham in Northumberland in England were asked to vote. The descriptions of the plans have been simplified and the effects on council tax have been rounded and simplified. They chose the most expensive option (4). The children could also read about issues which affect their local area and hold a debate about what should be done. They could write letters to their local council or to a local newspaper to communicate the result of their debate. This provides links with literacy (writing letters and writing persuasive texts).

> **Vocabulary:** *advantage, council, councillor, council tax, debate, disadvantage, discuss, election, issue, local, option, vote.*

# In the media – what's the news?

These activities are about the role of the local and national media – newspapers, radio, television, films and the Internet – in communicating topical local and national news. The children

develop skills of enquiry and an understanding of the responsibility involved in reporting news. They learn the importance of collecting evidence to support their views. All the work in this unit can be linked with work in literacy lessons on newspaper reports. A useful website for the children to visit is Children's Express, a programme of learning through journalism for 8–18 year olds: www.childrens-express.org.

**On balance** (page 61) helps the children to distinguish between fact and opinion in news reports. After completing this activity they could enact a discussion in which they present the views of different people: for example, a smoker, a bar worker, a waiter, someone who suffers from asthma or another respiratory disease or a restaurant or bar owner. How would a smoking ban affect these people?

> **Vocabulary:** *article, balance, bias, biased, fact, information, news, opinion, report, unbiased.*

**Headline news**, **Newsmaker** and **News writer** (pages 62–64) develop the children's knowledge of different sources of news and how these sources tailor news reports to suit their target audience. They have opportunities to work together and co-operate in groups and learn to recognise that the creation and presentation of information and news involves responsibility. Finally, they write a short article on a subject of interest to their readers. On page 62 they discuss what kind of news matters most for local, national and international newspapers and why some news is given more prominence than others. The newspapers used for this activity should be from the same day (any day during the current week). Show the class a children's TV news programme such as the BBC's Newsround from the same day as the newspaper articles. Are the main stories the same as those in the newspapers they reviewed? If not, why not? Discuss what the children could do if they were worried or frightened by something they read, heard or saw in the news – emphasise that the story is 'news' because it is an unusual event. Newsround features an online guide 'What to do if the news upsets you' http://news.bbc.co.uk/cbbcnews/hi/guides/default.stm. Page 63 and 64 require the children to work in groups to produce an end-of-term class newspaper. They need to agree how editing decisions will be made, perhaps by electing an editor or an editorial board, and what information to publish to interest their target audience. Each member of the group could take responsibility for a particular section of the newspaper: main news, important school events, class events, and so on. Groups of children could take turns to publish the newspaper each term. It is important to emphasise that this is non-fiction writing and that in reporting news about people the children have a responsibility to ensure that the facts are accurate. Also encourage them to think about whether it is ethical to report certain events (they could consider the importance of the privacy of individuals and their families). Ensure the children understand the responsibility they have to their group for carrying out the task they have undertaken. These sheets can be linked with work in literacy on reading and writing newspaper reports and there are opportunities to use ICT in creating a class newspaper, including the use of graphics such as art, graphs and photographs.

> **Vocabulary:** *article, balance, bias, biased, fact, importance, information, international, issue, local, national, news, opinion, report, story, unbiased.*

# To walk or not to walk

**Should children walk to school?**

- **Discuss this question with a partner.**
- **Write the results of your discussion.**

| Reasons for | Reasons against |
|---|---|
|  |  |
|  |  |
|  |  |
|  |  |
|  |  |
|  |  |
|  |  |
|  |  |

- **Write your answer.** _____

  _____

- **Write your partner's answer.** _____

  _____

- **Discuss how you can find out how many children walk to your school and to other local schools, and what factors influence this.**

**Teachers' note** Remind the children about what they have learned about holding a discussion with a partner (how to be a good listener). They might find it easier to discuss the issue if they do so without writing notes at first. They can then recap and make notes about what they said for and against the question.

**Developing Citizenship
Year 5**
© A & C BLACK

# Action for activity: 1

**How could your journey to school help to keep you fit?**

_____

_____

- **Discuss anything that makes this difficult.**
- **Take turns to list the problems.**

Work with a partner.

_____

_____

_____

_____

_____

_____

_____

_____

_____

_____

_____

_____

_____

- **Group the problems under headings such as _Dangers_, _Time_, _Distance_ and any others you need.**

**Teachers' note** The children could prepare this for homework. Ask them to talk to their parents or carers about the reasons for their choice about how they make their journey to school. While pointing out the health benefits of walking, it is also important to acknowledge that it is not easy, and sometimes not possible, for everyone to walk to school (or travel by bike or wheelchair).

**Developing Citizenship**
**Year 5**
© A & C BLACK

# Action for activity: 2

**What could be done to help you to be active on your way to school?**

- Work in a group.
- Brainstorm solutions to one of the problems you listed.

Record all the ideas before you discuss any of them.

- Solution 1
- Solution 2
- Solution 3
- Solution 4
- Solution 5
- Solution 6

Problem

**Which solution does your group think is best?**

- **Explain your answer.**

Now try this!

Do some research to support your answer.

**Teachers' note** The children should first have completed page 14. Invite feedback about their journeys to school, including any problems faced by those who walk (or cycle or travel in a wheelchair) to school or who want to do so.

**Developing Citizenship**
**Year 5**
© **A & C BLACK**

# Into action

The children at **Greenwood Primary School** agreed that it was not safe to walk along a road with no pavement.

They did a survey and drew a map.

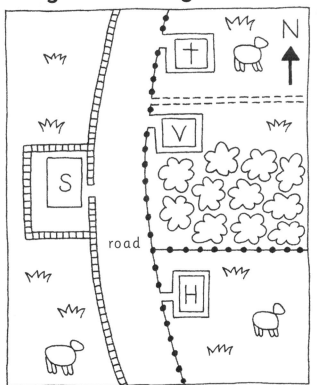

road just wide enough for 2 trucks to pass

not a main road but a through route

20 vehicles in 5 minutes

some fast: speed limit 60 mph

no room for a pavement

no lights

We want to ask the farmer who owns the land west of the road if we can make a footpath along the edge of the field.

**Key**

| | | |
|---|---|---|
| S school | ✝ church | V vicarage | ⁓ fields | H house |
| ⊞ wall | = = = farm track | •–• fence | woods | sheep or cattle |

- **Work in a group.**
- **Make a list of things the children should do next.**

Think about …

… letters to write …

… costs …

… who will be affected …

… who pays …

… who will do what …

… where the money comes from …

- **Write a group letter to the farmer supporting the children's plan and explaining your reasons.**

**Teachers' note** Ask the children about the dangers that could be faced during a walk to school. What types of roads are dangerous? Draw out that not only main roads can be dangerous; traffic can be a hazard wherever there are pedestrians, especially if they are close to the traffic. Discuss the actions the children in this example could take to keep safe: wearing clothes which make them easy to see and walking in single file.

**Developing Citizenship
Year 5
© A & C BLACK**

# These things matter

These questions are about things that matter to you.

- **Work with a partner.**
- **Write brief answers.**
- **Share your answers.**

Ask your partner about his or her answers.

What makes you happy?

_____

What would make you happier?

_____

What makes you unhappy?

_____

What single change would improve your school?

_____

What single change would improve your local community?

_____

What is the most unfair thing you have seen or heard about in your neighbourhood?

_____

What is the kindest thing you have seen or heard about in your neighbourhood?

_____

Now try this!

- **Write an explanation of one of your partner's answers.**

**Teachers' note** You could introduce this by answering the first three questions yourself, asking another adult to do the same and then sharing your answers and asking one another questions to find out more about what matters to the other person. Model how to be a good listener and how to encourage a partner to talk about things that matter.

**Developing Citizenship
Year 5**
© A & C BLACK

# Think about it

STOP!

Actions have consequences.

**These children have a choice. Their choice has** consequences.

- **Write three consequences of each action:**
  **for people, for animals and for the environment.**

| Choice | Consequences |
|---|---|
| Drop the litter | 1 _____<br>2 _____<br>3 _____ |
| Put the litter into a bin | 1 _____<br>2 _____<br>3 _____ |
| Recycle the litter | 1 _____<br>2 _____<br>3 _____ |

Now try this!

- **Design a poster to encourage others to think about what they choose to do with litter.**

**Teachers' note** Ask the children about some of the choices they make every day: for example, what to wear, what to eat, what to say to people they meet and how to say it, what to do at playtime, and so on. Encourage them to think about how their choices affect themselves and other people. Remind them of the meaning of the word *consequences*.

**Developing Citizenship
Year 5**
**© A & C BLACK**

# Recycle it

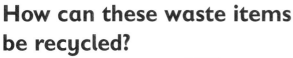

## How can these waste items be recycled?

- **Fill in the chart.**

Use leaflets, newspapers and the Internet.

| Object or material | Made into new material | Used for spare parts | Re-used |
|---|---|---|---|
| plastic bottle | ✔ | | ✔ |
| | | | |
| | | | |
| | | | |
| | | | |
| | | | |
| | | | |
| | | | |
| | | | |
| | | | |
| | | | |
| | | | |

Now try this!

- **Find out more about recycling one of these objects or materials.**
- **Write instructions to help someone to make sure it is re-used.**

---

**Teachers' note** Discuss what kinds of objects and materials can be recycled. Establish that some objects can be re-used (possibly after being repaired or reconditioned) whereas others can be taken apart and used for spare parts. Point out that some materials can even be made into new materials.

**Developing Citizenship**
**Year 5**
© A & C BLACK

# Chocolate choice

**What influences your choice of chocolate?**

The taste.  Special offers.  Organic.  Fairtrade.  Value for money.

☐     ☐     ☐     ☐     ☐

**Your choice can affect the lives of cocoa growers.**

- **Find out about Fairtrade from www.fairtrade.org.uk.**

| What Fairtrade does | How this helps growers |
|---|---|
|  |  |
|  |  |
|  |  |
|  |  |

Now try this!

**How is Fairtrade different from many other chocolate producers?**

- **Write a report about Fairtrade.**

**Teachers' note** Ask the children to think about things they buy or others buy for them. How do they choose what to buy? Ask them if they think the choices we make when we buy things affect other people and, if so, which people. Examples include shop-owners, companies which produce goods and raw materials, transport companies and their workers. Do the children think all these workers are paid fairly? Tell them why Fairtrade was founded (see **Notes on the activities**, page 6).

**Developing Citizenship**
**Year 5**
© **A & C BLACK**

# Making a difference

**How well is Fairtrade doing in your local community?**

- **Use this page to plan a survey of local shop-owners and shoppers.**

| Question | How we shall find out | Answer |
|---|---|---|
| Which Fairtrade goods are sold locally? | | |
| What percentage of local shops stock Fairtrade goods? | | |
| What percentage of shoppers know about Fairtrade? | | |
| What percentage of shoppers buy Fairtrade goods? | | |
| What percentage would buy Fairtrade goods if they were available? | | |

Now try this!

- **Write a list of ideas to support Fairtrade in your school and local community.**
- **Explain how these will help to promote fair trade.**

**Teachers' note** Ask the children if they have ever bought Fairtrade goods and whether they would do so if they had the choice (even if the cost is slightly higher than that of other goods). Do they know if Fairtrade goods are sold locally? Different groups could be taken to different shops to find out what Fairtrade goods are available locally, and shoppers could be asked for their views on Fairtrade goods.

**Developing Citizenship**
**Year 5**
© **A & C BLACK**

# Time to sell

## When are different goods advertised on television?
- **Carry out a survey to find out.**

**You need**
television advertisements recorded at different times of the day

We are looking at advertisements shown between _____ and _____ .

*Write the times.*

| Goods advertised | Target user | Target purchaser |
|---|---|---|
|  |  |  |
|  |  |  |
|  |  |  |
|  |  |  |
|  |  |  |
|  |  |  |

**What patterns did you notice?** _____

**Why do you think this was?** _____

**Now try this!**

- **Choose one advertisement.**
- **Explain how it makes the goods attractive to its target audience.**

**Teachers' note** Ask the children what kinds of goods are advertised on television. Which ones do they see advertised during the intervals between children's television programmes? Discuss whether the same goods are advertised at other times of the day. Draw out that advertisements are made for particular audiences and broadcast at times when those audiences are most likely to be watching.

**Developing Citizenship**
**Year 5**
© A & C BLACK

# Zoo talk

**Is it wrong to keep animals in zoos?**

- **Discuss this with your group.**
- **Write a summary of the discussion.**

| For zoos | Against zoos |
|---|---|
|  |  |
|  |  |
|  |  |
|  |  |
|  |  |
|  |  |
|  |  |
|  |  |
|  |  |
|  |  |

- **Present your views during a class debate.**
- **Hold a secret ballot using the voting slip.** ☒

It [is] wrong to keep animals in zoos. ☐

It [is not] wrong to keep animals in zoos. ☐

- **Use the chart to help you to write a radio script of an argument between two people, one in favour Zof zoos and one against.**

**Teachers' note** The children could discuss the question without making notes and then summarise their discussion, with all members of the group making notes on the key points raised for and against zoos. During another lesson they could present their views in a class debate in which two children present an argument supporting zoos and two present an argument against them. Use the voting slip after the debate.

**Developing Citizenship**
**Year 5**
© A & C BLACK

# Hedgehog helper

- **Read the information about hedgehogs.**
- **Discuss it with your group.**
- **Write a list of actions people can take to care for hedgehogs.**

---

### DANGER TO HEDGEHOGS

In October the hedgehog begins to prepare for the winter. It builds up body fat through feeding on small animals such as beetles, caterpillars, slugs and worms. It will also eat cat and dog food and bread, although bread makes it ill. It builds a nest from twigs and leaves in any suitable area – usually on the ground. Some favourite sites for nests are piles of wood, leaves and garden waste. The hedgehog hibernates from about November to March.

When faced with danger the hedgehog curls into a ball. Its spines protect it from predators, such as eagles, foxes, owls, polecats and snakes. However, no animal has the hedgehog as its staple diet.

Hedgehogs are protected by law. It is illegal to kill them; nonetheless their greatest threat is from humans, who kill them accidentally. Between 50,000 and 100,000 hedgehogs are killed on the roads each year, but many more are killed in other ways. They roll into steep-sided ponds and cattle grids and drown or become trapped. They are burnt or suffocated when fires are lit to burn garden waste in which they are hibernating. Many are killed by lawnmowers and strimmers. They eat slug pellets and pesticides.

---

Now try this!

- **Design a leaflet advising people how to protect hedgehogs.**

Find out more from wild animal welfare websites.

---

**Teachers' note** Ask the children about animals they see harmed by accident: for example, on the roads; because people damage the animal's habitat; or because people give it foods which they do not realise can harm it. Do they know about the dangers hedgehogs face from people? Invite them to give examples before they read the passage.

**Developing Citizenship Year 5**
© A & C BLACK

# Hedgehog-friendly school

**How hedgehog-friendly is your school?**

- **Carry out an investigation.**
- **Draw ☺ or ☹.**
- **Score 1 point for each ☺ and take off 1 point for each ☹.**

Even a school with tiny grounds can be hedgehog-friendly.

| Hedgehog-friendly | ☺ | Not hedgehog-friendly | ☹ |
|---|---|---|---|
| Wild areas with plants to attract insects and other minibeasts | | Pesticides | |
| Piles of leaves in which hedgehogs can nest | | Netting for plants | |
| Adults who burn rubbish checking for hedgehogs first | | Not checking rubbish before burning it | |
| Ponds with a sloping side so that hedgehogs can get out | | Steep-sided ponds | |
| Water, especially in very hot or freezing weather | | Slug pellets | |
| Litter always in bins | | Litter on the ground, especially tins, jars and plastic bags | |
| Total | | Total | |

- **Discuss with your group what you can do to make your school grounds more hedgehog-friendly.**
- **Write your ideas.**

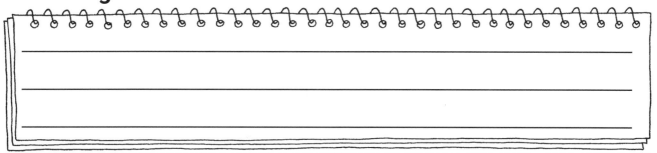

Now try this!

- **Plan a campaign to encourage others in your school to be hedgehog-friendly.**
- **Work with a partner to design a campaign poster.**

**Teachers' note** Give the children information leaflets or web articles about the dangers facing hedgehogs. Ask them what people can do to avoid harming hedgehogs. How hedgehog-friendly do they think the school grounds are? Take them out to investigate the grounds. Ask them about the other people who would need to be involved in making the area hedgehog-friendly.

**Developing Citizenship**
**Year 5**
© **A & C BLACK**

# Five freedoms

The **RSPCA** wants all pets, working animals and farm animals to have 'Five freedoms'.

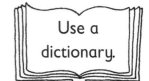

**RSPCA** stands for Royal Society for the Prevention of Cruelty to Animals.

- **Discuss the 'Five freedoms' with a partner.**
- **Choose any pet, working animal or farm animal.**
- **Write what the animal's owner should do to give it the 'Five freedoms'.**

Animal: _____

Use a dictionary.

| Five freedoms | What the owner should do |
|---|---|
| Freedom from hunger and thirst | |
| Freedom from discomfort | |
| Freedom from pain, injury and disease | |
| Freedom to express normal behaviour | |
| Freedom from fear and distress | |

Now try this!

- **What should be done if an animal's owner does not give it the 'Five freedoms'?**
- **Write a letter to tell your local Member of Parliament about your ideas.**

**Teachers' note** Ask the children if they can think of any rules that people who keep animals should follow. They could discuss these with their groups and write a list. Invite feedback before the children undertake the activity on this page; ask the class to vote for the five most important rules. They could compare their list with the 'Five freedoms' suggested by the RSPCA.

**Developing Citizenship**
**Year 5**
© **A & C BLACK**

# The law in action

**You need**

news reports about cruelty to animals

People who harm animals can be taken to court and punished.

- Read some examples from news reports.
- Make notes on the chart about each case.

| Headline of story | Type of animal | How it was harmed | How the person was punished | What happened to the animal |
|---|---|---|---|---|
| | | | | |
| | | | | |
| | | | | |
| | | | | |

Now try this!

- Choose one story.
- Describe the roles of the police, the RSPCA and the court.

**Teachers' note** Ask the children about the ways in which some people are cruel to animals, and discuss why. Draw out that often this is because they do not have the right type of places in which to keep them, underestimate the amount of time and attention the animals need or their circumstances change. Discuss deliberate cruelty and encourage the children to imagine the feelings of the animals. Provide each group with a collection of news reports about cases of cruelty to animals (see **Notes on the activities**, page 7).

**Developing Citizenship**
**Year 5**
© A & C BLACK

# Emergency call

**You should call 999 only for emergencies.**

**The police treat the following as emergencies:**

1. someone's life is in danger
2. a vulnerable person is at risk
3. a crime is in progress or immediate action is needed to get evidence
4. there has been a road collision involving serious injury or causing serious traffic congestion
5. public disturbance or disorder is happening

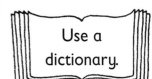
Use a dictionary.

- **Discuss with a partner what these mean.**
- **Give an example of each one.**

| Emergency | Example | Other emergency services needed |
|---|---|---|
| 1 | | |
| 2 | | |
| 3 | | |
| 4 | | |
| 5 | | |

Now try this!

- **Find out how your local police force aims to respond to 999 calls.**

Read their charter. Find it on their website.

**Teachers' note** Ask the children what they know about making 999 calls (when and how). Discuss the meaning of the five emergency situations described on this page, including vocabulary such as *collision, congestion, disorder, disturbance, evidence, in progress, vulnerable.* Remind the children that there are four emergency services: ambulance, coastguard, fire brigade and police.

**Developing Citizenship**
**Year 5**
**© A & C BLACK**

# Police help

You might need help from the police with something which is not an emergency.

• **Give four examples.**

a _____

b _____

c _____

d _____

**How could you contact the police?**

• **Give four ways of doing this.**

1 _____

2 _____

3 _____

4 _____

If you are not sure, find out from your local police force.

• **Find out what the police might do in one of the examples you gave.**

Example: _____

Police action: _____

_____

_____

_____

Now try this!

• **Write a storyboard for a 30-second television advertisement to tell people how to contact the police in a non-emergency situation.**

**Teachers' note** Before the children begin this page ask them about the occasions on which they or their families have asked for help from the police in non-emergency situations. Examples could include: finding their home has been burgled, theft of a car or other property, lost property, someone acting suspiciously. How did they contact the police? They could telephone, e-mail, write, visit a police station or tell an officer on the beat. How did the police help them?

**Developing Citizenship**
**Year 5**
© **A & C BLACK**

# Keep out crime

Everyone can help to stop crime.

The police give this advice to adults.

How can children help?

| Police advice | How children can help |
|---|---|
| Always know where your children are and whom they are with. | |
| Be a good neighbour. | |
| Try to help people when they need it. | |
| Tell us if you see a crime or anything suspicious and try to remember details such as car registration numbers. | |
| Have good lighting around your home and garden, including timer switches and sensors. | |
| Fit British Standard door locks – and use them. | |
| Always lock your car, even in the garage. Take out the keys, especially when paying for petrol. Never leave anything on view. | |
| Make a note of serial numbers of valuables. Use a property marker to label valuables with your postcode. | |
| Do not put bank or credit card statements in household waste. | |

Now try this!

- **Find out about the Neighbourhood Watch scheme.**
- **Write a crime prevention leaflet for children.**

**Teachers' note** Ask the children what they think is the purpose of the police: draw out that they maintain law and order. How do they do this? Establish that, as well as detecting crime and arresting people caught committing crimes or suspected of having done so, the police try to prevent crime. Ask the children to name some crimes and to suggest ways in which people can protect themselves in order to reduce the risk of being a victim of each crime.

**Developing Citizenship Year 5**
© A & C BLACK

# Crime report

- ## Discuss this crime with a partner.

| Friday 10:00pm | Saturday 9:00am | Saturday 10:00am |
|---|---|---|
|  |  |  |
| Yusuf sees a car outside Mrs Nash's house. The driver is a woman. A man gets out and goes round to the back of the house. After a while, he comes back with a bag and gets into the car. The car moves off. | Mrs Nash returns home from a night at her daughter's house. She enters the house and finds that her belongings have been damaged and some valuables are missing. She calls the police. | A police officer calls at Yusuf's house. She asks Yusuf's father if he or his family saw anyone going into Mrs Nash's house the night before. |

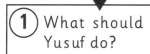 (1) What should Yusuf do?

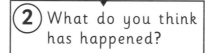 (2) What do you think has happened?

(3) What should Yusuf do?

- ## Discuss these questions with your partner.
- ## Write your answers.

(1) _____

_____

(2) _____

_____

(3) _____

_____

Now try this!

## What might worry Yusuf if he talks about what he saw?
- ## Write some advice for Yusuf.

**Teachers' note** After the children have discussed the crime story in pairs, invite feedback. Emphasise that they should not approach anyone acting suspiciously. Safe ways of helping to prevent a crime of this type include telling a responsible adult what they have seen. Discuss what might stop people reporting someone acting suspiciously or giving evidence (see **Notes on the activities**, page 8).

**Developing Citizenship**
**Year 5**
© **A & C BLACK**

# Town and country

**Do you live in a town or a country place?** _____

**How would living in the country or town be different?**

• **Discuss this with a partner.**

• **Write your ideas.**

| Town | Country |
|------|---------|
| _____ | _____ |
| _____ | _____ |
| _____ | _____ |
| _____ | _____ |
| _____ | _____ |
| _____ | _____ |
| _____ | _____ |

• **Find out if your ideas are correct.**

You should talk to, e-mail or write to children at another school.

We were right about _____

_____

_____

We were wrong about _____

_____

_____

**Now try this!**

• **Write a magazine article comparing town and country life.**

**Teachers' note** Discuss the different meanings of *country* ('an area with its own government and flag' and 'a rural area' – introduce the term *rural*) and explain that in this activity *country* means a rural place. Ask the children to think about the characteristics of towns and rural places before considering how these differences might affect people's everyday lives.

**Developing Citizenship**
**Year 5**
© A & C BLACK

# A visit to Chinatown

Part of Liverpool is called 'Chinatown' because it has had a large Chinese community since the nineteenth century.

Children from a Liverpool school planned a visit to Chinatown.

- Read their notes and questions.
- Add some of your own.

| Notes: what we know about the Chinese community | Our questions |
|---|---|
| Chinatown around Berry St, Upper Duke St, Nelson St<br>Chinese pagoda<br>Chinese arch decorated in red and yellow<br>Pictures of dragons | Why did the Chinese immigrants come to Liverpool? Why did they settle in this part of Liverpool? |

**Now try this!**

- **Find the answers to the questions.**
- **Write a report about Chinatown.**

Visit www.chinatown-online.co.uk.

**Teachers' note** Read the introduction to this activity with the children and ask them what they would expect to see if they visited Chinatown (in Liverpool or another city – see **Notes on the activities**, page 8). What special characteristics would this part of the city have? What would they like to know about it?

**Developing Citizenship
Year 5
© A & C BLACK**

# Finding out

- **Find out about a community which came to your region from another region or country.**

  The community is _____.

- **Write notes on the chart.**

| Where the people came from | Where the people have settled | Why they came |
|---|---|---|
| _____ | _____ | _____ |
| _____ | _____ | _____ |
| _____ | _____ | _____ |
| _____ | _____ | _____ |

**Special features of the community**

_____

_____

_____

Think about language, art, music, dance, food and customs.

_____

_____

_____

**What the community has given to our region**

_____

_____

Think about the arts, buildings, industry, services, entertainment and festivals.

_____

_____

Now try this!

- **List five ways in which you can find out more about this community.**

**Teachers' note** In preparation for this activity, children whose families came to this country as immigrants could set up displays of artefacts and pictures relating to their cultural heritage. Or the activity could follow a visit to an area which is rich in a cultural heritage with its origins overseas: places of worship, restaurants, shops, and so on. Before photocopying this sheet, fill in the name of the community being investigated by the class.

**Developing Citizenship**
**Year 5**
© A & C BLACK

# Kick out racism

- ## Discuss these reports with a partner.
  ## What could the people there have said or done?

When Manchester United's German goalkeeper, Bert Trautmann, first joined them in 1949 the crowd chanted 'Heil Hitler'.

_____

_____

_____

_____

_____

1998

Any darkies in your team today?

Two football club chairmen

_____

_____

_____

_____

_____

1999

You're a team full of niggers.

Sunderland fans at a match against Newcastle United

_____

_____

_____

_____

_____

2000

Supporters of Yugoslavia made monkey noises whenever Emile Heskey had the ball when he played for the England Under-21 team.

_____

_____

_____

_____

Now try this!

- ## Collect other examples of racist behaviour in sport.
- ## Explain why they are racist.
  ## What could people who were there have said or done?

**Teachers' note** This page presents genuine examples of football racism from 1998–2000 reported on the website www.kickitout.org and in _The Week_. Draw out that racism includes using offensive language when talking _about_ people's religion or country of origin as well as verbally or physically abusing them. After completing the activity, the children could discuss the words which are and are not acceptable for describing people's ethnicity.

# Accident aware: 1

Most schools have places, substances and equipment which are dangerous if not used properly.

Which of these does your school have?

| Places | How they could harm |
|---|---|
|  |  |

| Substances | How they could harm |
|---|---|
|  |  |

| Equipment | How they could harm |
|---|---|
|  |  |

Now try this!

Sometimes work has to be done which causes risks for a short time.

- List some precautions taken to minimise these temporary risks.

**Teachers' note** Discuss why there are harmful substances, equipment and places in school and how the school protects children (and adults) from danger. Draw out that these things are safe when used by people who know how to use them: for example, boilers, electrical equipment, ovens, hobs, chemicals used for cleaning. During the plenary session draw out the consequences which could arise from improper use.

**Developing Citizenship Year 5** © A & C BLACK

# Accident aware: 2

**How does your school keep you safe?**

- **Make notes about any risks you find and how you are kept safe.**

**You need**

your school's health and safety policy and guidelines

What could harm you?

How does your school keep you safe?

---

Now try this!

- **Discuss each risk with a partner.**
- **Write suggestions about what you should do to stay safe.**

---

**Teachers' note** This activity could be introduced by reading the school's health and safety policy and guidelines as a shared reading activity. Encourage the children to question anything they do not understand. The children could refer to the risks they listed on page 36 and find out from the guidelines what the school does in order to create a healthy and safe environment.

**Developing Citizenship**
**Year 5**
**© A & C BLACK**

# Over to you

**What kinds of accidents do children sometimes cause to themselves and to one another at school?**

- **Discuss this with your group.**
- **Make notes about the points discussed.**

| In the classroom | Around the school |
|---|---|
| _____ | _____ |
| _____ | _____ |
| _____ | _____ |
| _____ | _____ |
| _____ | _____ |

**Accidents**

| In the playground | On the way to school |
|---|---|
| _____ | _____ |
| _____ | _____ |
| _____ | _____ |
| _____ | _____ |
| _____ | _____ |

- **Choose one type of accident.**
- **Collect suggestions from other people in the school about how to prevent it.**

Now try this!

- **Use a computer to design notices to help to prevent one kind of accident at school.**

Give advice about safe behaviour.

**Teachers' note** This could be used as a follow-up to pages 36 and 37. Having listed the potentially dangerous places, substances and equipment and made notes about the actions the school takes to keep everyone safe, the children should consider their own responsibilities for their safety and that of others. Draw out that the safety of any place requires the co-operation of everyone who uses it.

**Developing Citizenship**
**Year 5**
© **A & C BLACK**

# Cost it

Sometimes a school would have to spend money to make a place or some equipment safe.

Could anything be made safer at your school? How?

• **Discuss this with your group.**

This could be made safer: _____
_____

Our ideas for making it safer: _____
_____
_____
_____
_____
_____

The solution we chose: _____
_____

| Cost | | | |
|---|---|---|---|
| **Materials** | **£** | **Work** | **£** |
| | | | |
| | | | |
| | | | |
| | | | |
| | | | |

• **Write a letter to your school council or headteacher to describe your idea.**

**Teachers' note** This page could be used in relation to any safety issue which the children decide requires action. This could include dangerous materials, the safety of pedestrians on paths around the school, the security of substances and equipment, and so on. The school council in one school asked for security fencing because of break-ins. The headteacher told them the cost and how this would affect the budget for equipment, school trips, and so on.

**Developing Citizenship**
**Year 5**
**© A & C BLACK**

# Charter of rights

What rights do you think all children should have?

- **Work in a group to write a charter of rights for all children.**

A charter is a list of conditions to which people agree.

### Charter of rights for children

_____

_____

_____

_____

_____

_____

_____

_____

_____

_____

_____

_____

_____

_____

- **Work in a group.**
- **Prepare a presentation about children's rights and who should uphold them.**

**Teachers' note** Before the children begin this activity it is important to discuss the meanings of *rights*, *needs* and *wants* and to ensure that the children are able to distinguish between these. Explain that a charter is based on the promises of those who sign it. Encourage the children to think about needs such as security, love, education, medical care. Is it sufficient to have a home, a place to sleep and enough to eat and drink? What else do all children need?

**Developing Citizenship Year 5**
© **A & C BLACK**

# The rights of the child

In 1989 the following ten rights for children were agreed by many countries.

- Discuss these rights with your group.
- Think about what is `fair` and `unfair` and write how these rights help.

| Children's rights | How they help things to be fair |
|---|---|
| 1 All children have the following rights, no matter what their race, colour, gender, language, religion, political or other opinion, where they were born or whom they were born to. | 1 _____ _____ |
| 2 To grow up and to develop physically and spiritually in a healthy and normal way, free and with dignity. | 2 _____ _____ |
| 3 To have a name and to be a member of a country. | 3 _____ _____ |
| 4 To have access to care and protection, clean water, good food, housing and medical services. | 4 _____ _____ |
| 5 To receive special care if they have a disability. | 5 _____ _____ |
| 6 To be given love and understanding, preferably by parents and family, otherwise by the government. | 6 _____ _____ |
| 7 To receive free education, time to play and an equal chance to develop and to learn to be responsible and useful. Parents have special responsibilities for a child's education and guidance. | 7 _____ _____ |
| 8 Always to be among the first to get help when it is needed. | 8 _____ _____ |
| 9 To be protected against cruel acts or exploitation. Not to have to work before a minimum age and never when that would damage their health or moral and physical development. | 9 _____ _____ |
| 10 To be taught peace, understanding, tolerance and friendship among all people. | 10 _____ _____ |

- **Choose one of these rights.**
- **Write a report about a time in the past when some children were not allowed this right.**

**Teachers' note** The children could compare this list with their own lists (see page 40). Are there any rights which they did not think of? Do they agree with the official list? Explain what UNICEF is (see **Notes on the activities**, page 10) and explain that UNICEF drew up the Convention on the Rights of the Child and that many countries have signed it and have promised to uphold these rights.

**Developing Citizenship**
**Year 5**
© **A & C BLACK**

# ActionAid

- **Find out how ActionAid helps to give children the ten rights listed on page 41.**

Look at the work of ActionAid around the world.

**act:on**aid

Write to:
ActionAid
Hamlyn House
Macdonald Road
London N19 5PG

phone: 020 7561 7561

or visit:
www.actionaid.org.uk

| Right | Country | How ActionAid helps |
|-------|---------|---------------------|
| 1 | | |
| 2 | | |
| 3 | | |
| 4 | | |
| 5 | | |
| 6 | | |
| 7 | | |
| 8 | | |
| 9 | | |
| 10 | | |

Now try this!

- **Write a short report about one of the examples above.**

**Teachers' note** This could be introduced through work in geography on the work of ActionAid in countries such as India. It could also be linked with work on democracy. Ask the children what ActionAid does in order to be democratic. (The views of the people are sought; they are encouraged to take part in village councils. They are asked what kind of aid they would find useful: for example, in Khalipathar, Orissa, they asked for wells to be repaired and for new wells to be dug.) **Developing Citizenship Year 5** © A & C BLACK

# Children's responsibilities

- **Find out about one of ActionAid's projects.**

**What** responsibilities **do the children there have?**

How do the children help to look after their homes, schools and villages?

| Responsibility | How it helps to uphold their rights and those of others |
|---|---|
| | |

- **Compare these children's responsibilities with yours.**
- **Write about the similarities and differences.**

**Teachers' note** Ask the children about their responsibilities at home. How do they spend their time? What do they do to help in the running of their homes? Discuss the effects on a home or other place if everyone who is able takes some responsibility for looking after it and for caring for the other people who live there.

**Developing Citizenship Year 5**
© A & C BLACK

# That's a lie

• **Discuss the picture story with your group.**

8:30am

Is it OK if I go to Rashid's house after school, Dad?

OK, but be home by 5.30.

Patrick

8:30am

May I go to Patrick's after school, Mum?

Yes, as long as his dad knows.

Rashid

3:30pm

Let's go to town. They'll never know.

## What did Patrick and Rashid do wrong?

_____

_____

_____

_____

Give two wrong actions.

## Why were their actions wrong?

_____

_____

_____

_____

Give as many reasons as you can.

Now try this!

**Why do you think Patrick and Rashid did not ask if they could go to town?**

**What should they have done if they wanted to be allowed to go?**

• **Write about the choices they had.**

**Teachers' note** Ask the children to comment on lies told by characters in stories they have read. Why did the characters tell lies? Examples include avoiding doing something they do not want to do, to keep out of trouble, or to have or do something they are not allowed. What were the consequences of these lies? Draw out that often a lie leads to the need to tell more lies.

**Developing Citizenship Year 5**
© A & C BLACK

## The Bully Asleep

One afternoon, when grassy
Scents through the classroom crept,
Bill Craddock laid his head
Down on his desk, and slept.

The children came round him:
Jimmy, Roger and Jane;
They lifted his head timidly
And let it sink again.

'Look, he's gone to sleep, Miss,'
Said Jimmy Adair:
'He stays up all the night, you see;
His mother doesn't care.'

'Stand away from him, children.'
Miss Andrews stooped to see.
'Yes, he's asleep; go on
With your writing, and let him be.'

'Now's a good chance!' whispered Jimmy;
And he snatched Bill's pen and hid it.
'Kick him under the desk, hard;
He won't know who did it.'

'Fill his pockets with rubbish –
Paper, apple-cores, chalk.'
So they plotted, while Jane
Sat wide-eyed at their talk.

Not caring, not hearing,
Bill Craddock he slept on;
Lips parted, eyes closed –
Their cruelty gone.

'Stick him with pins!' muttered Roger.
'Ink down his neck!' said Jim.
But Jane, tearful and foolish,
Wanted to comfort him.

John Walsh

---

**Teachers' note** The poem could be read with the whole class to introduce this activity. Discuss the character of Bill Craddock and how we know what he is like (from the words of the other children). Which children want to hurt him, and why? Why does his teacher let him sleep at school?

**Developing Citizenship**
**Year 5**
© A & C BLACK

- **Work with a partner.**
- **Answer the questions.**

What facts can you find out about Bill Craddock from the poem?

_____

_____

What wrong things do the children do to Bill Craddock?

_____

_____

What wrong things do they talk about doing to him?

_____

_____

What do you think has made them want to behave like this towards him?

_____

_____

_____

What do you think might have made Bill Craddock bully other children?

_____

_____

Which two children show some understanding of Bill Craddock's feelings, and how can you tell?

_____

_____

_____

**What do you think might make some children bully others?**

**Teachers' note** Ask the children how they feel about Bill Craddock. What makes the reader feel sympathy for him? What difference would it make if the poem described Bill Craddock bullying the others rather than their responses to it? Draw out that sometimes people bully others because they are not happy (but stress that this behaviour is still not acceptable).

**Developing Citizenship
Year 5**
© A & C BLACK

# Ground rules

**What rules are followed when you have a discussion with your group?**

- **Discuss this question with a partner.**
- **Write your ideas on the notepad.**

*Does everyone have to say something?*

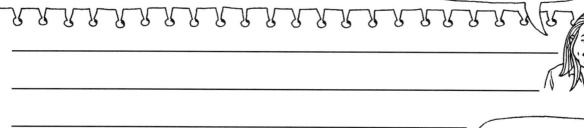

*What would encourage group members to join in?*

*What should you do when someone is speaking?*

*What should you not do?*

- **From your notes write six rules.**

1 _____

2 _____

3 _____

4 _____

5 _____

6 _____

Now try this!

**What could your group do to ensure that the six rules are obeyed by everyone?**

- **Write about how the group could be organised to ensure the rules are kept.**

**Teachers' note** This activity could be used following any group or class discussion. There may be no written rules, but what rules do the children follow so that everyone has the chance to speak and to be listened to? Ask them to think about how they can encourage others to express their views and find out more about others' views. How can they make one another feel at ease (including not feeling under pressure to say anything if they do not want to)?

**Developing Citizenship**
**Year 5**
© A & C BLACK

# Democracy

Democracy is when everyone has a say in what happens in their country or community.

It is not practical to ask *everyone* about every issue …

I think …

We should …

We could …

… so people vote for people to represent them.

**Which of these would you choose to represent your class?**

The most important thing is to listen to people.

Gurdeep would keep a notebook of his classmates' concerns.

☐

I would have a suggestions box.

Alice would hold a weekly meeting to discuss the suggestions to find out who agreed with them.

☐

I would try to interest everyone in security at school.

Gary is concerned about break-ins. He wants to make school safer.

☐

• **Explain why you would vote for this person.**

Now try this!

**Do you think school or class council members should be changed each term or each year?**

• **Write reasons for your answer.**

**Teachers' note** This could be used to introduce the idea of a school or class council. If there is already a school or class council, this could be used to look at the ways in which council members are chosen. It introduces the criteria used for choosing and encourages the children to think about what the nominees can offer, rather than just choosing their friends. Draw out that democracy gives everyone a chance to be represented in decision-making.

**Developing Citizenship Year 5**
**© A & C BLACK**

# Democracy in action

**How good are your school or class rules?**

- **Discuss them with your group.**
- **Make notes about your discussion.**

What changes could be made?

What rewards or punishments could be changed?

Which rules are broken most often? What should be done?

**You need**

a copy of your school or class rules

**How can a school or class council help?**

- **Write your group's ideas.**

**Now try this!**

- **Write a newspaper report about how a school council helped to make a change.**

**Teachers' note** Put the children into groups for this activity. It could be used following any incidents in which school or class rules are disobeyed or which are not addressed by existing rules. There could be rules which the children feel are no longer needed. It could also be an opportunity to alter the words used to express rules or to give a positive evaluation where the children are satisfied with the rules.

**Developing Citizenship**
**Year 5**
© **A & C BLACK**

# Criminal record

These people have a criminal record .

What might happen when they try to find work?

- **Write in the thought bubbles.**

> I'd like to deliver papers for the newsagent.

Lisa is 13. When she was 11 she was found guilty of shoplifting.

Mrs Khan, the newsagent

_____
_____
_____
_____

> I could find work in a shop on Saturdays.

Zul is 15. He had an Anti-Social Behaviour Order and was not allowed out after 7pm because he had damaged neighbours' property.

Mr Rose, the shop manager

_____
_____
_____

> I'd like to be a vet.

Gwyneth is 16. She has been fined for being drunk and disorderly in the town centre.

Mrs Kay, the university admissions tutor

_____
_____
_____
_____

Now try this!

- **Find out what happens when someone has a criminal record.**

For more information see www.rizer.co.uk.

**Teachers' note** Ask the children at what age they think people can be held responsible by law for their actions, and can therefore have a criminal record if they break the law (ten crin England and Wales but eight in Scotland). Ask them how they think other people might react if they know someone has a criminal record. Draw out why they might have trouble finding certain types of work, and for how long (see **Notes on the activities**, pages 10–11).

**Developing Citizenship Year 5**
**© A & C BLACK**

# Shoplifted

**THIEVES PUT FUTURE OF STORE IN DOUBT**

A local shopkeeper is about to close her doors following shoplifting that has cost nearly £7,000 in a year. Vivien Martin has run a grocery store for 10 years and £2,000 a year spent on CCTV cameras and a 24-hour alarm has not stopped the thieves. She even sealed her letterbox after cameras showed thieves using a long pole to drag out crisps and biscuits at night.

Mrs Martin said that the police have done such an excellent job in the city centre that the thieves have moved to the suburbs. She explained that costs make it not worth taking them to court.

"I call the police and they come and arrest them. But they do not prosecute for the theft of an item costing a few pounds because it is seen as a waste of taxpayers' money …"

Mrs Martin added that she is not suffering alone and thinks she knows why the majority steal: "I know many stores where shoplifting is a problem, and I think most of it is done by those with drug problems."

Mrs Martin has had to think about her future: "If it continues, I shall close the shop. Then this community will have no corner shop."

Adapted from *This is Herefordshire*

- **Read the newspaper report with a partner.**
- **Discuss what it tells you about shoplifting.**
- **Make notes on a chart like this:**

| Why people shoplift | What happens to shoplifters who are caught | How shoplifting affects shopkeepers | How shoplifting affects the local community |
|---|---|---|---|
|  |  |  |  |

Now try this!

- **Find out how other shoplifters are punished.**
- **Notice any similarities and differences.**
- **Discuss with a partner whether the punishments are fair.**

You could find the answers from the Internet or police visitors.

**Teachers' note** Read the newspaper report with the children and ask them what facts it gives. What opinions does it give? This could lead to discussions about why people steal from shops. After they have completed the activity, draw out the effects of shoplifting on shopkeepers, their families and the local community, in particular elderly people and those who have no car.

**Developing Citizenship**
**Year 5**
© **A & C BLACK**

# Red-handed

- **Work with a partner.**

  **Mrs O'Marr sees Nina putting a box of sweets in her pocket. Nina does not pay for it.**

- **Discuss what Mrs O'Marr could do.**
- **Write her options in the boxes.**

| ① | ② |
|---|---|
| ③ | ④ |

**How might each of these affect Nina?**

① _____

_____

② _____

_____

③ _____

_____

④ _____

_____

- **Discuss which of these is the best option.**
- **Say why.**

Now try this!

- **Write what you would say to Mrs O'Marr to persuade her to choose the option you think is best.**

**Teachers' note** After the children have completed the page, ask them to think what made Nina steal the sweets but pay for the comic. What could have stopped her stealing? Invite feedback about Mrs O'Marr's responses: for example, she might ask Nina if she had anything else to pay for, ask if she had forgotten about the sweets, accuse her of stealing them, call the police. Which would be the most likely to stop Nina stealing again, and why?

**Developing Citizenship**
**Year 5**
© **A & C BLACK**

# Open space

- **Work in a group.**
- **Photograph or sketch a public open space in your local area.**
- **Discuss this place with your group.**
- **Write notes.**

**You need**

camera
clipboard
paper
pencil

| Features | Advantages of these features | Disadvantages of these features |
|---|---|---|
| | | |
| | | |
| | | |
| | | |
| | | |
| | | |
| | | |

| Who uses this place | How they use it |
|---|---|
| | |
| | |
| | |

**How can this place be improved?**
- **Think about:**
  - **how it can be made more pleasant**
  - **how it can be made easier to use.**

**Teachers' note** This should be used to identify the features of a local open space: for example, a small grassy corner with a bench, a village green, a small public garden or a shopping mall. Draw out the ways in which the open space is useful to people or makes the area more pleasant. Discuss the effects of vandalism in this place: for example, parents might not want to take children there; dog owners might avoid it if dangerous litter were discarded there.

**Developing Citizenship**
**Year 5**
© **A & C BLACK**

# Damage survey

**How do people damage public places?**

Work with a group.

- **Carry out a survey in a place in your local area.**
- **Arrange the cards in order:**

Not a problem ⟶ A major problem

| | |
|---|---|
| broken glass | broken seats and other equipment |
| damaged trees and other plants | damaged lawns |
| damaged signs | chewing gum |
| dog fouling | graffiti |
| anti-social behaviour | theft |
| | |

Now try this!

- **Find out what is being done about vandalism in your area.**

**Teachers' note** The children should discuss the cards with their groups, identify any other forms of damage which are not included (for example, noise from shouting, loud music or machinery) and write these on the blank cards. They could take turns to place a card on a 'ladder' drawn on paper with rungs numbered upwards, and to move one of the other cards if necessary. They should justify the place they give to any card they move or add to the ladder.

**Developing Citizenship**
**Year 5**
© A & C BLACK

# Vandal busters

Ask your local council for information.

- **Work with a group.**
- **List the three main types of vandalism in a public place you know.**
- **Discuss what can be done about them.**

| Type of vandalism | Ways of preventing it | Punishment for vandals |
|---|---|---|
|  |  |  |
|  |  |  |
|  |  |  |

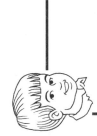

Now try this!

- **Work with a partner.**
- **Find out more about one type of vandalism.**
- **Write a report on what can be done about it and how much this would cost.**

Developing Citizenship
Year 5
© A & C BLACK

**Teachers' note** This activity is best undertaken following page 54. After agreeing which are the main vandalism problems in a public open space, the children should discuss each one in turn and make notes about their ideas for preventing it (see **Notes on the activities**, page 11). The local council might be able to provide information on how it deals with vandalism and what this costs. Ask the children to compare the costs of prevention and repairs.

# Changing places

What  facilities  does your local area have? ✔

• **Write how they could be improved.**
  **What facilities would you like to have?** ✔

| Facility | Has | How it could be improved | Would like |
|---|---|---|---|
| park | | | |
| sports field | | | |
| tennis courts | | | |
| playground | | | |
| cycle tracks | | | |
| footpaths | | | |
| swimming pool | | | |
| library | | | |
| golf course | | | |
| cinema | | | |
| theatre | | | |
| community centre | | | |
| | | | |
| | | | |

• **Share your answers with your group.**
  **Which facility does the group think would improve the area the most?**

_____

• **Draw and write a plan for a new facility for your local area.**

**Teachers' note** Introduce the word *facilities* and ask the children for examples. They could use this page or use a computer to create their own survey page listing different facilities from those shown here, or making changes to suit their needs. The graph on page 57 could be used with this page or the children could use data-handling software.

**Developing Citizenship
Year 5
© A & C BLACK**

# Facilities survey

**What facilities would people in your local community like improved?**

- **Carry out a survey.**
- **Make a note of the results.**
- **Present the results as a graph.**

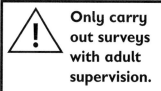

Only carry out surveys with adult supervision.

Each group could ask 10 or 20 people.

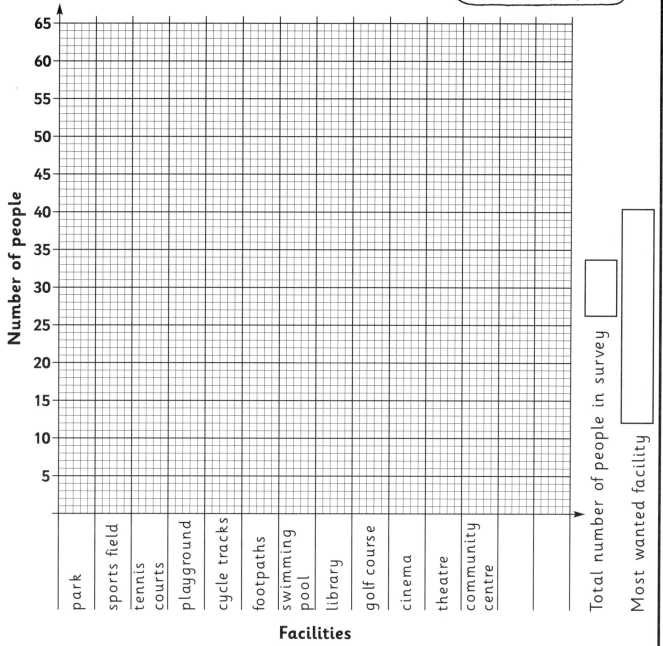

**Number of people**

65
60
55
50
45
40
35
30
25
20
15
10
5

park
sports field
tennis courts
playground
cycle tracks
footpaths
swimming pool
library
golf course
cinema
theatre
community centre

**Facilities**

Total number of people in survey

Most wanted facility

Now try this!

- **Think about possible sites for the most wanted facility.**
- **Draw a map and describe the best site.**

**Teachers' note** This is designed to accompany page 56 or the children could use data-handling software to record, sort and present the results of their survey. Ask them which facility is the most wanted. What could be done about this? Discuss whom the children could contact, and how.

**Developing Citizenship**
**Year 5**
© A & C BLACK

# Local council

- **Find out about your local council.**

Name of council _____

**For which of the following is the local council responsible?**

collecting waste ☐

libraries ☐

shops ☐

schools ☐

weather forecasts ☐

roads ☐

fire service ☐

police ☐

television ☐

hospitals ☐

parks ☐

water supply ☐

Now try this!

- **Find out how your local council runs one of the above services.**
- **Write a report about it.**

**Teachers' note** Ask the children about the services everyone needs and which any settlement (hamlet, village, town, city) needs: for example, water, drains, rubbish collection, roads, road maintenance and cleaning, footpaths (and maintenance and cleaning), fire brigade, police, hospitals, doctors, and so on. Do they know who is responsible for providing these and who pays for them?

**Developing Citizenship Year 5**
© A & C BLACK

# Councillor

- **Find out about the work of a local councillor.**

Use your local council's website or information leaflets.

| Name of councillor | How to contact the councillor |
|---|---|
| **Ward (the area he or she looks after)** | |
| **How a councillor is elected** | |

| Your questions about council work | Answers |
|---|---|
| ① | ① |
| ② | ② |
| ③ | ③ |

Now try this!

- **Find out what a councillor can do if people in the ward ask for action:**
  **for example, to make a road safer to cross.**

**Teachers' note** This activity can be carried out using printed or electronic information from the local council, but would be enhanced by a visit from a local councillor, who could tell the children about the work he or she does, for how long and how he or she came to do this work.

**Developing Citizenship**
**Year 5**
© A & C BLACK

# Debate it

## This is the choice faced by a town council.

A great deal of repair work is needed to the swimming pool, the pumping and filtering equipment and the building itself. The car park is too small. There are no other leisure facilities in the building. More changing space and a separate learners' pool are needed. The pool is too small to have parts sectioned off for leisure swimming during school or swimming club sessions. More than 110,000 visits per year are made to the pool. The population of the area served by the council is 58,808. The options are:

1. Close the pool and sell the building. This would reduce council tax by about £4 per year for each household. There is no other swimming pool in the town.
2. Repair and refurbish the pool and building. This would increase council tax by about £8. The pool would have to close for about 12 months. Car parking would not be changed. The pool size and changing areas could not be increased.
3. Close the pool and build a new one at the leisure centre (on the site of the bowls hall). This would increase council tax by about £6. The old pool could be used while the work was in progress. A bigger pool could be built with a separate learners' pool and larger changing areas. There is no other bowls hall in the area.
4. As for option 3 and build a new bowls hall, adding about £10 to council tax.

- ## List the advantages and disadvantages of each option.

| Option | Advantages | Disadvantages |
|---|---|---|
| ① | | |
| ② | | |
| ③ | | |
| ④ | | |

My choice is Option _____ because _____

_____

- ## Imagine you are a local councillor.
- ## Prepare a speech to persuade the council to follow your suggestion.

**Teachers' note** This could be linked with page 59: a local councillor could tell the children about a council decision – including whether the elected members made the decision or people in the area were asked to vote on it. Draw out that it is not feasible to ask people to vote on every decision but that sometimes this does happen. Encourage the children to find out what people can do to influence the council's decision or if they are not happy about a decision it has made.

**Developing Citizenship**
**Year 5**
© **A & C BLACK**

# On balance

- **Discuss this news report with a partner.**
- **Underline** bias **or opinion in red.**
- **Underline facts reported without bias in green.**

> Reporting other people's opinions is not the same as expressing an opinion yourself.

---

### ALL PUFFED OUT

Smoking is to be banned in all cafes and restaurants in England. Pubs which serve food will also be barred from letting customers or staff light up. A ban on smoking in all work-places is also included in the Government's White Paper on health, which will be unveiled by Health Secretary John Reid today.

When the plans come into force in two to three years' time smokers will only be allowed to indulge their habit publicly in a pub not serving food. Publicans of such premises – and it is thought that snacks such as crisps and peanuts do not count – will be able to choose on lighting up. But more than half of English pubs are expected to introduce a ban because of the food rule.

The Government has been under intense pressure to introduce a ban in England. Ireland went smoke-free earlier this year followed by Scotland last week.

In a *Daily Mirror* poll last week, 58 per cent of readers wanted a complete ban. Dr Reid had been tipped to back away but seems to have been swayed by the strength of public opinion.

Adapted from *Daily Mirror*, Nov 16 2004

---

**Which colour have you mainly used?** _____

**Is the report** biased **or** unbiased **?** _____

- **Re-write the report in two different ways:**
  1 **Agreeing with the ban.**
  2 **Disagreeing with the ban.**

> Unbiased reporting gives facts and tries to present a balance of opinions.

---

- **Look for a news report which is biased.**
- **Re-write it so that it is unbiased.**

**Teachers' note** The children should find this report unbiased. It presents mainly facts. The opinions are estimates ('more than half of English pubs *are expected* to …') rather than the writer's views on the issue. You could also draw attention to the language used; there are no examples of connotations which communicate an opinion.

**Developing Citizenship
Year 5**
© A & C BLACK

# Headline news

**What is on the front pages of today's newspapers?**

- **Scan the headlines and skim-read the text.**

International, national or local?

**You need**

international, national and local newspapers for the same day

| Name of newspaper | I, N or L | Main news story | Other important news stories |
|---|---|---|---|
|  |  |  |  |
|  |  |  |  |
|  |  |  |  |
|  |  |  |  |
|  |  |  |  |

Now try this!

**How do you think newspaper editors decide which story to feature as the main news?**

- **Write your ideas.**

**Teachers' note** It is useful first to discuss the meanings of *local*, *national* and *international* and what counts as local, national or international news. Ask the children what has been in the local news. Was this also in the national or international news? Discuss why or why not. Where do people find out about local, national and international news? Do the different media (the Internet, newspapers, radio, television) give the same news?

**Developing Citizenship Year 5**
**© A & C BLACK**

# Newsmaker

- **Work with a group.**
- **Plan a class newspaper for the end of term.**
- **Each take responsibility for one section of the newspaper.**

**Main news**

Headline _____

Facts

What is the most important news or issue?

| **Important school events** | **Class events** |
|---|---|
| **Our good news** | **Our family news** |

**Features and reviews**

Check the facts. You have a responsibility to get them right.

**Now try this!**

- **Design the front page of your newspaper.**

Use a computer.

**Teachers' note** Discuss the kinds of news or features which would interest the pupils of the school. How will the children decide which is the main news? Draw out that front-page news should be about an event or issue which affects or would interest the whole school, rather than only one or two children or one class. Who should take responsibility for editing decisions? The groups might want to elect an editor or they might prefer to form an editorial board.

**Developing Citizenship**
**Year 5**
© **A & C BLACK**

# News writer

- **Use this page to plan an article for a class newspaper.**
**Your limit is 100 words.**

Will it be a news story about a school or class event? Or will it be a feature or a review?

**Type of article**

_____

**Headline**

_____

**Introduction** _____

_____

_____

Should this story be told? Are you being fair to the people in it?

**Paragraph 1** _____

_____

**Paragraph 2** _____

_____

**Paragraph 3** _____

Are you sure that the story is true? Check the facts.

_____

**Conclusion** _____

_____

_____

Summarise the main points or repeat a point made in the introduction.

Now try this!

- **Word-process your article and check the number of words.**
- **Swap with a partner and edit one another's work.**

**Teachers' note** Ask the children to plan in their groups who will be responsible for each aspect of writing the class newspaper. Ask them to consider whether their writing is a recount of an event, a report, argument or discussion about, or explanation of, an issue. Ask them to consider how formal their writing should be and how this affects the type of language they will use. Emphasise their responsibility to the people in their stories and to their readers to be accurate, fair and clear.

**Developing Citizenship**
**Year 5**
© **A & C BLACK**